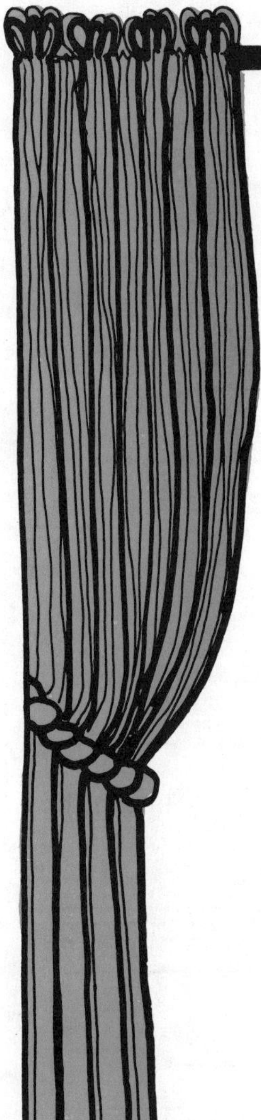

Level 2

PIANO RECITAL SOLOS

**by Jane Smisor Bastien
and
James Bastien**

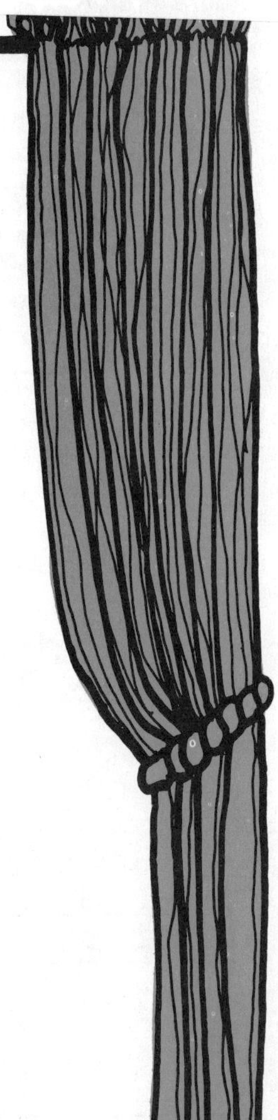

Contents

Title	Page
Clouds	8
Ghosts Dance on Halloween	12
Indian Ceremonial	2
March Militaire	4
Pioneer Days	14
Pirate Island	10
Scat Boogie	6

ISBN 0-8497-5098-9

Indian Ceremonial

for Irene Struve

JANE SMISOR BASTIEN

With a steady beat

f
p
cresc.
ff
5
2
f
5
2
mf
cresc.
ff
8va

for Deanne Harmon

March Militaire

FRANZ SCHUBERT
Arr. by James Bastien

Tempo di marcia

cresc.

for Vicky Anderson

Scat Boogie

JAMES BASTIEN

r. h.
cresc.
r. h.
f
mf
f
mf
rit.
8va

for Clarice Lincoln

Clouds

Stems up = R.H.
Stems down = L.H.

JAMES BASTIEN

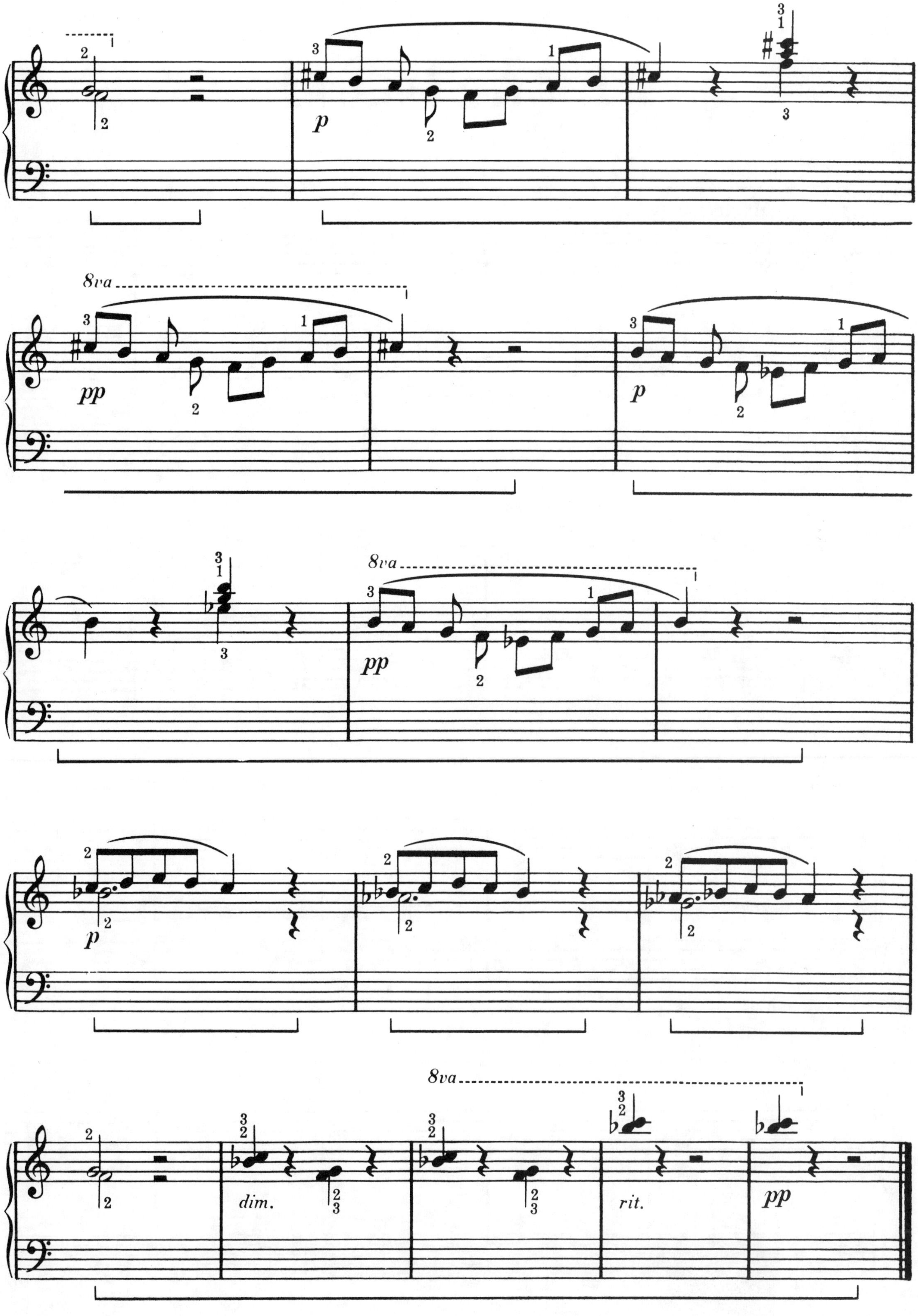
p
8va
pp
p
8va
pp
p
8va
dim.
rit.
pp

for Sister M. Immaculate Serverino

Pirate Island

JAMES BASTIEN

p
f
p
f
f
p
f
mp
mp

f
8va

for Ken Miller

Ghosts Dance on Halloween

JANE SMISOR BASTIEN

cresc.
mf
f
8va

for Lucy Chu

Pioneer Days

JANE SMISOR BASTIEN

cresc.
ff
a tempo
f
cresc.
ff

POP PIANO STYLES

A light and refreshing collection of rock, blues, boogie, and disco styles from Jane and James Bastien. From foot-stompin' rhythms to melancholy moods, these up-to-date sounds encourage practicing and performing for pianists of all ages!

Levels 1-4

Level 1
WP51

Level 2
WP52

Level 3
WP53

Level 4
WP54